CONTENTS

MW01031704

ISBN 0-8497-6275-8

2

Unit 1
Rhythm

1. Add bar lines to divide each rhythm into equal measures. Write the counts for each rhythm on the line under the staff.

2. Draw one note at the end of each measure to complete the correct number of beats.

3. Determine the correct time signature for each example and write it at the beginning of each staff.

Unit 2
Key Signatures

The Circle of Keys

The **circle of keys** is a diagram of all Major and minor key signatures. The sharp keys are arranged from the top, moving clockwise. The flat keys are arranged from the top, moving counter clockwise.

There are fifteen Major keys: seven sharp keys, seven flat keys, and one key with no sharps or flats. Likewise, there are fifteen relative minor keys.

The keys at the bottom of the circle are called **enharmonic** keys because their tones sound the same but are named and written differently.

The circle of keys is sometimes called the **circle of fifths** because the keys are arranged an interval of a fifth apart. Notice that as you move around the circle clockwise from the top, one new sharp is added to each key. As you move around the circle counter clockwise from the top, one new flat is added to each key.

Writing the Circle of Keys

1. Write the name of each Major and minor key on the lines outside of the circle.
   Write the sharps and flats for each Major and minor key on the staffs inside the circle.

   Do as much as you can from memory. Check your answers by referring to the
   Circle of Keys on page 4.

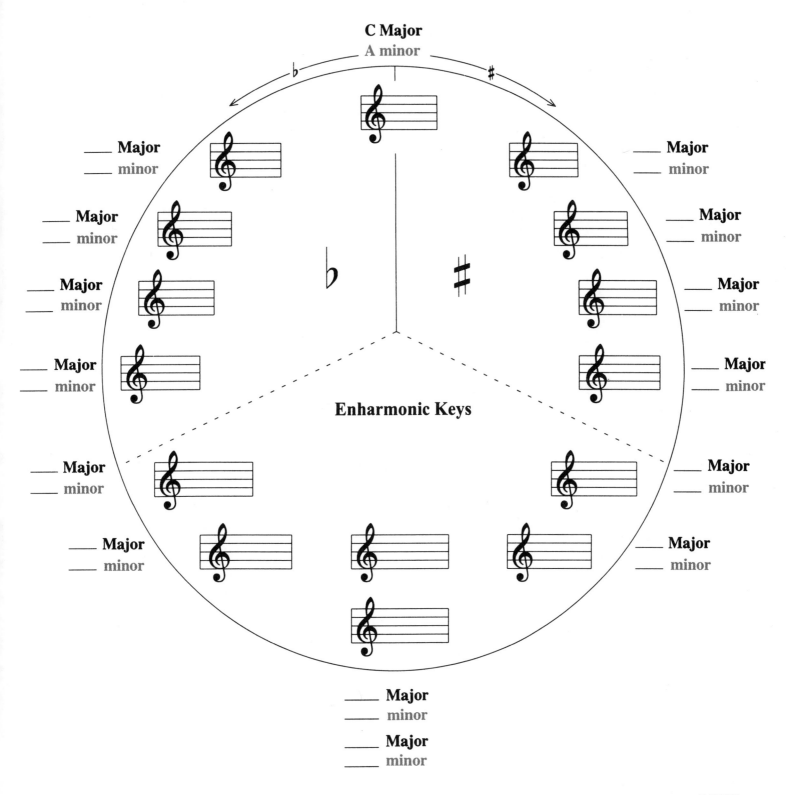

6

2. Write the Major and minor name for each key signature.

_____ Major   _____ Major   _____ Major   _____ Major   _____ Major

_____ minor   _____ minor   _____ minor   _____ minor   _____ minor

_____ Major   _____ Major   _____ Major   _____ Major   _____ Major

_____ minor   _____ minor   _____ minor   _____ minor   _____ minor

_____ Major   _____ Major   _____ Major   _____ Major   _____ Major

_____ minor   _____ minor   _____ minor   _____ minor   _____ minor

3. Write each key signature.

D Major   C minor   E Major   B♭ minor   F♯ Major

A♭ minor   G Major   G minor   A Major   F minor

B Major   E♭ minor   C♯ Major   D minor   A minor

Unit 3
Scales

Major Scales

All **Major scales** are formed with the same pattern of half steps and whole steps:
whole - whole - **half** - whole - whole - whole - **half**

1. Add the correct sharps or flats to form each Major scale (do not use a key signature).
   Check your answers by referring to the Circle of Keys on page 4.

2. Draw the notes of each Major scale. Add the correct sharps or flats to form each scale
   (do not use a key signature).

Relative Minor Scales

Each Major scale has a relative minor scale with the same key signature.
The 6th note of the Major scale is the 1st note of the relative minor scale.

3. Draw the notes of each Major and relative minor scale indicated by the key signature.

4. Write the key signature indicated, then draw the notes of the minor scale.

Forms of Minor Scales

There are three forms of minor scales: **natural, harmonic, melodic.** The **natural** minor scale follows the key signature exactly: none of the notes are changed. The **harmonic** minor scale has a raised 7th note (1/2 step). The **melodic** minor scale has a raised 6th and 7th note ascending, and then lowered descending. The melodic minor scale descending uses the same notes as the natural minor scale. The altered notes in the harmonic and melodic minor scale must be written in as accidentals.

5. Change these natural minor scales to **harmonic** minor scales by adding the correct accidentals.

6. Change these natural minor scales to **melodic** minor scales by adding the correct accidentals.

Parallel Major and Minor Scales

Parallel Major and minor scales have the **same** tonic note.
They have **different** key signatures.

6. Write the key signature for each scale, then draw the notes for each scale.

7. The music excerpt below changes key after each repeat sign. One key change is to a parallel key, and the other key change is to a relative key. Study the music and name each key.

From *Rondo alla Turca* by Mozart
(Piano Repertoire: Baroque & Classical, Level 8, page 40)

Whole Tone Scale

A **whole tone scale** is made entirely of whole steps. There are only two sets of tones upon which a whole tone scale may be formed. Each set has six tones.

Set 1

Set 2

A whole tone scale can begin on any note. The notes can be written with a variety of enharmonic spellings, for example:

 or

1. Draw six notes to complete each whole tone scale.

2. Rewrite each whole tone scale with enharmonic spellings for the notes that are sharp or flat.

Unit 4
Intervals

The distance between two notes is called an **interval.**

Interval Qualities

- 2nds, 3rds, 6ths and 7ths may be Major, minor, diminished or Augmented.
- 4ths, 5ths and 8ths (octaves) may be Perfect, diminished or Augmented.

Harmonic and Melodic Intervals

Two notes played together form a **harmonic** interval. Two notes played one at a time form a **melodic** interval.

1. Identify each interval. Write **M** for Major, **m** for minor, **P** for Perfect, **d** for diminished and **A** for Augmented.

2. Draw a note above the given one to form each interval.

M3   P5   m3   d5   A4   m6   M3   P4

m3   P5   m7   A2   M6   M7   m2   M3

3. Write the name of each interval on the lines above and below these music excerpts.

From *Variations, Op. 40, No.1* by Kabalevsky
(Piano Repertoire: Romantic & 20th Centrury, Level 8, page 76)

From *Sonata, Op. 49, No. 1,* by Beethoven
(Piano Repertoire: Baroque & Classical, Level 8, page 46)

From *Invention No. 13* by J.S. Bach
(Piano Repertoire: Baroque & Classical, Level 8, page 9)

Unit 5
Triads

G Major Triad

A **triad** is a three note chord. The notes of a triad are called the root, 3rd, and 5th. The root names the triad.

Triad Qualities

Triads may be Major, minor, diminished or Augmented. The **Major** triad has a Perfect 5th and a Major 3rd. The **minor** triad has a Perfect 5th and a minor 3rd. The **diminished** triad has a diminished 5th and minor 3rd. The **Augmented** triad has an Augmented 5th and a Major 3rd.

1. Name each triad. Write **M** for Major, **m** for minor, **dim.** for diminished and **Aug.** for Augmented.

2. Write these triads.

GM   Gm   G dim.   G Aug.   EM   Em   E dim.   E Aug.

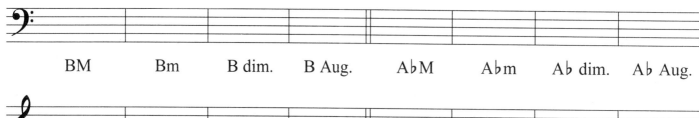

BM   Bm   B dim.   B Aug.   A♭M   A♭m   A♭ dim.   A♭ Aug.

FM   Fm   F dim.   F Aug.   AM   Am   A dim.   A Aug.

Triads and Inversions

All triads have two **inversions.** A triad is in **root position** when the root of the triad is the lowest note. A triad is in **1st inversion** when the 3rd of the triad is the lowest note. A triad is in **2nd inversion** when the 5th of the triad is the lowest note.

3. Draw the inversions of these root position triads.

Figured Bass for Triads and Inversions

Figured bass is the use of numbers to identify the inversion of a triad. The figured bass numbers identify the intervals of a triad measured from the bass note (lowest note). The figured bass for a root position triad is $\frac{5}{3}$, however, figured bass is usually omitted for root position triads. The figured bass for a first inversion triad is $\frac{6}{3}$, usually abbreviated to 6. The figured bass for a second inversion triad is $\frac{6}{4}$.

4. Name each triad and write the figured bass.

Triads of Major Scales

A triad may be built on each degree of the Major scale. Each triad is labeled with a Roman numeral.

Major = upper case Roman numeral
minor = lower case Roman numeral
diminished = lower case Roman numeral and °

Each triad is named after the scale degree name of its root.

C Major

I	ii	iii	IV	V	vi	vii °	I
Tonic	Supertonic	Mediant	Subdominant	Dominant	Submediant	Leading Tone	Tonic

1. Write the Roman numeral and figured bass for each triad of the E Major scale on the lines below the staff. Write the scale degree name for each triad on the lines above the staff.

2. Draw each triad of the B♭ Major scale according to the Roman numerals and figured bass. Write the scale degree name for each triad on the lines above the staff.

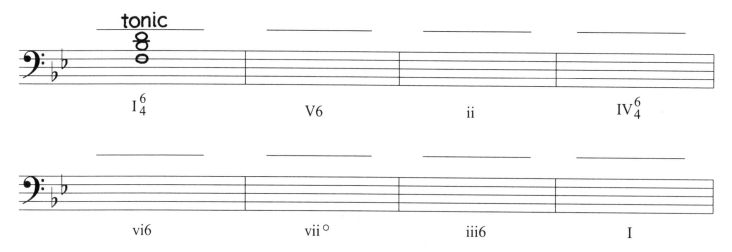

Triads of Minor Scales (Harmonic Form)

A triad may be built on each degree of the minor scale. Each triad is labeled with a Roman numeral.

Major = upper case Roman numeral
minor = lower case Roman numeral
diminished = lower case Roman numeral and °
Augmented = upper case Roman numeral and +

Each triad is named after the scale degree name of its root.

i	ii°	III+	iv	V	VI	vii°	i
Tonic	Supertonic	Mediant	Subdominant	Dominant	Submediant	Leading Tone	Tonic

3. Write the Roman numeral and figured bass for each triad of the D minor scale on the lines below the staff. Write the scale degree name for each triad on the lines above the staff.

4. Draw each triad of the F♯ minor scale according to the Roman numerals and figured bass. Write the scale degree name for each triad on the lines above the staff.

i$^6_4$ VI6   V   III+6

iv$^6_4$ vii°6   ii°   i6

GP668

Unit 6
Seventh Chords

A seventh chord is a four note chord. The notes of a seventh chord are called the root, 3rd, 5th, and 7th.

Seventh Chord Qualities

Five qualities of seventh chords are shown below. These seventh chords are formed with the following combinations of triads and 7ths:

- **Major Seventh Chord**: Major triad plus a Major 7th.
- **Dominant Seventh Chord**: Major triad plus a minor 7th.
- **Minor Seventh Chord**: minor triad plus a minor 7th.
- **Half Diminished Seventh Chord**: diminished triad plus a minor 7th.
- **Diminished Seventh Chord**: diminished triad plus a diminished 7th.

1. Draw Major, Dominant, minor, half diminished and diminished seventh chords on the given roots.

2. Name each seventh chord.

Seventh Chords and Inversions

All seventh chords have three inversions.

3. Draw the inversions of each root position seventh chord.

Figured Bass for Seventh Chords and Inversions

Figured bass is used to identify the position of a seventh chord. The figured bass numbers identify the intervals of a seventh chord measured from the bass note (lowest note). The figured bass for a root position seventh chord is $\frac{7}{5}$, abbreviated to 7. The figured bass for a 1st inversion seventh chord is $\frac{6}{5}$, abbreviated to $\frac{6}{5}$. The figured bass for 2nd inversion seventh chords is $\frac{6}{4}$, abbreviated to $\frac{4}{3}$. The figured bass for 3rd inversion seventh chords is $\frac{6}{4}$, abbreviated to $\frac{4}{2}$ or 2.

4. Name each seventh chord and write the figured bass.

GP668

Seventh Chords of Major Scales

A seventh chord may be built on each degree of the Major scale. Each seventh chord is labeled with a Roman numeral and figured bass. Seventh chords built on the tonic and subdominant notes (I and IV) are Major seventh chords. Seventh chords built on the supertonic, mediant and submediant notes (ii, iii and vi) are minor seventh chords. The seventh chord built on the leading tone (vii) is a half diminished seventh chord. The seventh chord built on the dominant note (V) is the dominant seventh chord.

5. Write the Roman numeral and figured bass for each seventh chord of the D Major scale.

6. Write the Roman numeral and figured bass for each seventh chord of the E♭ Major scale.

7. Draw the dominant seventh chord for each key according to the figured bass.

Diminished Seventh Chords

The diminished seventh chord can be built on the leading tone of the harmonic minor scale.

The diminished seventh chord is unique because the root, 3rd, 5th and 7th are all a minor 3rd apart. On the keyboard, the distance between the notes will not change in any inversion. The chords will "feel" the same, but be spelled and written differently.

Any note of a diminished seventh chord can become the root by changing the spelling of the chord. Therefore, any note of a diminished seventh chord can become the leading tone of a scale. In the example below, the same diminished seventh chords as in the example above are written in root position. The root of each diminished seventh chord is functioning as a leading tone (vii) resolving to tonic (i).

Since any note of a diminished seventh chord can become the root, depending on the spelling of the chord, the diminished seventh chord is frequently used for modulation*. The diminished seventh chord can function like a secondary dominant (vii°7 of V, vii°7 of IV, etc.)**.

Although the diminished seventh chord can be built on the leading tone of the harmonic minor scale, diminished seventh chords are used in music in both Major and minor keys. In either a Major or minor key, accidentals must be used when writing a diminished a seventh chord.

From *Sonata, Op. 49, No. 1* (2nd mvt.) by Beethoven (*Piano Repertoire: Baroque & Classical*, Level 8, page 52)

8. Draw a diminished seventh chord before each given chord according to the figured bass.

*See Unit 8.   **See Unit 7.

GP668

Unit 7
Secondary Dominant

A **secondary dominant** is the dominant of a scale degree other than the tonic. Secondary dominants are labeled with Roman numerals designating them as V of ii, V of iii, V7 of IV, etc. Secondary dominants account for most of the accidentals found in music.

1. Play this chord progression which uses secondary dominants in the key of G Major.
   Then, transpose to the key of A Major.

2. Play this chord progression which uses secondary dominants in the key of D Major.
   Then, transpose to the key of B♭ Major.

3. Write the Roman numerals and figured bass for these chords.

4. Write the Roman numerals and figured bass for each underlined chord in the music excerpt below.

From *Sonata, Hob.XVI:35*, by Haydn
(*Piano Repertoire: Baroque & Classical*, Level 8, page 24)

5. Write the Roman numerals and figured bass for each underlined chord in the music excerpt below.

From *Invention No. 14*, by Bach
(*Piano Repertoire: Baroque & Classical*, Level 8, page 6)

Unit 8
Modulation

Modulation is a change of key within a composition: one key is left and a new one is established. Most modulations occur between keys that are closely related. Closely related keys are those which are adjacent on the circle of keys. The key signatures of closely related keys differ by no more than one sharp or flat. For example, music in the key of C Major frequently modulates to G Major or F Major, or to their relative minor keys of A minor, E minor, or D minor. Recurring accidentals generally indicate a modulation.

Modulation with a Secondary Dominant

Modulation is frequently established with a secondary dominant. The secondary dominant becomes the dominant of the new key. The music excerpt below begins in the key of C Major. The V7 of V in measure 23 establishes a modulation to the key of G Major.

From *Sonata, Hob.XVI:35*, 1st mvt., measures 22-25, by Haydn
(Piano Repertoire: Baroque & Classical, Level 8, page 24)

In polyphonic music, the notes of a chord are usually spread out in a melodic passage. The chords are often incomplete and merely implied by the notes of a melody. In the music excerpt below, a series of secondary dominants are outlined in the melodic lines. The music modulates quickly through several keys, culminating in an authentic cadence in C minor at measure 12.

From *Invention No. 14*, measures 8-12, by Bach
(Piano Repertoire: Baroque & Classical, Level 8, page 6)

* See Unit 9

Phrase Modulation

Phrase modulation is a sudden change of key between phrases. One phrase will cadence in the original key, and the next phrase begins immediately in the new key. In the music excerpt below, the first phrase cadences in E minor at measure 14. The second phrase modulates to G Major.

From *The Cuckoo,* measures 12-18, by Daquin
(Piano Repertoire: Baroque & Classical, Level 8, page 20)

Modulation with a Pivot Chord

Modulation can be established with a chord that exists in both the original key and the new key. This chord is used to **pivot** from the original key to the new key. The music example below modulates from C minor to E♭ Major. The modulation is established with a pivot chord: the iv chord in C minor is also the ii chord in E♭ Major.

From *Sonata, Hob.XVI:35,* 3rd mvt., measures 54-61, by Haydn
(Piano Repertoire: Baroque & Classical, Level 8, page 38)

Modulation to a Parallel Key

Music can modulate from a Major key to the parallel minor key, or a minor key to the parallel Major key. The modulation usually occurs when the key signature changes. The music excerpt below begins in G minor and modulates to G Major. Notice that the modulation actually occurs in the measure before the key signature change (B natural in the left hand).

From *Sonata, Op. 49, No. 1,* 2nd mvt., measures 78-83, by Beethoven
(Piano Repertoire: Baroque & Classical, Level 8, page 56)

1. In the music excerpt below, a modulation occurs with a secondary dominant. Label the underlined chords with Roman numerals and figured bass and name the key to which the music modulates.

From *Sonata, L. 58,* by Scarlatti
(Piano Repertoire: Baroque & Classical, Level 8, page 4)

D minor: ____ ____ ____   ____ ____ of ____ ____

____ minor: ____   ____   ____   ____

2. The music excerpt below modulates quickly through several keys using secondary dominants. Name the key to which each V7 chord belongs (for example: V7 of F).

From *Sonata, Hob.XVI:35,* by Haydn
(Piano Repertoire: Baroque & Classical, Level 8, page 28)

____ of ____   ____ of ____   ____ of ____

3. The music excerpt below is an example of a phrase modulation. Study the left hand chords to determine the key of the second phrase. Label the underlined chords with Roman numerals and figured bass.

From *Waltz, Op. 69, No. 1* by Chopin
(Piano Repertoire: Romantic & 20th Century, Level 8, page 21)

Key of A♭ Major   Key of _____

_____   _____   _____

4. The music excerpt below modulates with a pivot chord. Study the music in measures 5-8 to determine the key to which the music has modulated (look for a V7 chord!). Name the new key and label the underlined chords with Roman numerals and figured bass.

From *The Stranger,* measures 1-8, by Schumann
(Piano Repertoire: Baroque & 20th Century, Level 8, page 12)

Pivot
Chord

D minor: ____   ____   ____ ____

____ minor: ____   ____   ____ ____

Unit 9
Cadences

A **cadence** is the combination of two chords used at the end of a phrase, section, or piece of music. The various types of cadences are:

Authentic: V (or V7)-I   **Plagal**: IV-I   **Half**: any cadence ending on V (or V7)   **Deceptive**: V-vi

1. Write the Roman numerals for the underlined chords in each music excerpt. Then, write the name of the cadence on the line under the Roman numerals.

From *Echoes from the Theater* by Schumann
(*Piano Repertoire: Romantic & 20th Century*, Level 8, page 8)

Key of A minor

From *The Stranger* by Schumann
(*Piano Repertoire: Romantic & 20th Century*, Level 8, page 12)

Key of A minor

From *Prelude in E minor* by Chopin
(*Piano Repertoire: Romantic & 20th Century*, Level 8, page 17)

Key of E minor

From *Waltz in A♭* by Chopin
(*Piano Repertoire: Romantic & 20th Century*, Level 8, page 26)

Key of A♭ Major

From *Waltz in A♭* by Chopin
(*Piano Repertoire: Romantic & 20th Century*, Level 8, page 25)

Key of A♭ Major

From *Sonata in C, Hob.XVI:35* by Haydn
(*Piano Repertoire: Baroque & Classical*, Level 8, page 24)

Key of C Major

From *Sonata in G minor, Op. 49, No. 2* by Beethoven
(*Piano Repertoire: Baroque & Classical*, Level 8, page 46)

Key of G minor

From *Sonata in C, Hob.XVI:35* by Haydn
(*Piano Repertoire: Baroque & Classical*, Level 8, page 36)

Key of C Major

Unit 10

Chord Progressions: Modulation to the Dominant

A **chord progression** is a series of chords.

The chord progression below modulates for C Major to G Major (dominant key).

1. Write each chord progression according to the Roman numerals and figured bass.
   Play each chord progression.

F Major: I   V7 of V   V

C Major: I   ii6   I$_4^6$ V7   I

B♭ Major: I   V7 of V   V

F Major: I   ii6   I$_4^6$ V7   I

E♭ Major: I   V7 of V   V

B♭ Major: I   ii6   I$_4^6$ V7   I

C Major: I   V7 of V   V

G Major: I   ii6   I$_4^6$ V7   I

GP668

Unit 11
Augmentation and Diminution

Composers often vary a motive or phrase by changing the note values. When the note values are doubled, it is called **augmentation.** When the note values are halved, it is called **diminution***.

1. Play each phrase and count aloud.

2. Rewrite the melody below, first using diminution, then augmentation.

3. Study each music excerpt below and write augmentation or diminution on the line above the staff.

From *Dr. Gradus ad Parnassum,* by Debussy
(Piano Repertoire: Romantic & 20th Century, Level 8, page 41)

From *Sonatina, 3rd mvt.,* by Khachaturian
(Piano Repertoire: Romantic & 20th Century, Level 8, page 60)

*Although the ratio of 2:1 is most frequently used, others may be found.

Unit 12
Pedal Point

A **pedal point** is a consistent note that is held, repeated, or returned to regularly as harmonies change. It is usually in a low voice. The pedal point is not always a chord tone in the harmony above it. Shown below are three music excerpts that have pedal points.

From *Sonatina* by Khachaturian
(Piano Repertoire: Romantic & 20th Century, Level 8, page 64)

Repeated pedal point on D

From *Dr. Gradus ad Parnassum* by Debussy
(Piano Repertoire: Romantic & 20th Century, Level 8, page 41)

Held pedal point on A♭

From *Andante* by Burgmüller
(Piano Repertoire: Etudes, Level 8, page 15)

Regularly returned to pedal point on A

1. Name the note that is a repeated pedal point in the music excerpt below. _____

From *The Witch,* by MacDowell
(Piano Repertoire: Romantic & 20th Century, Level 8, page 36)

2. Name the note that is a regularly returned to pedal point in the music excerpt below. _____

From *The Witch,* by MacDowell
(Piano Repertoire: Romantic & 20th Century, Level 8, page 36)

Unit 13
Texture

Texture in music is the horizontal and vertical relationship of the notes in a composition. The two most common textures are **polyphonic** and **homophonic.**

Polyphonic Texture: Music with two or more independent parts or voices (melodies).

Keyboard music from the Baroque period is usually written in polyphonic texture. In the examples below, notice that each hand is playing single notes; each hand has its own melody.

From *Invention No. 13* by Bach
(*Piano Repertoire: Baroque & Classical,* Level 8, page 8)

From *Courante* by Telemann
(*Piano Repertoire: Baroque & Classical,* Level 8, page 14)

1. Write the name of a piece you have played that is polyphonic. _____

Homophonic Texture: Music with melody and accompaniment.

Music from the Classical and Romantic periods is usually written in homophonic texture. In the examples below, notice that the melody may be in the right hand or the left hand.

From *Prelude Op. 28, No. 6,* by Chopin
(*Piano Repertoire: Romantic & 20th Century,* Level 8, page 18)

From *Rondo all Turca* by Mozart
(*Piano Repertoire: Baroque & Classical,* Level 8, page 40)

2. Write the name of a piece you have played that is homophonic. _____

Most music actually exists somewhere between the extremes of polyphonic and homophonic texture. In the examples below, notice the use of both polyphonic and homophonic textures.

From *Sonata, L. 58,* by Scarlatti
(*Piano Repertoire: Baroque & Classical,* Level 8, page 4)

From *Prelude, Op. 28, No. 6,* by Chopin
(*Piano Repertoire: Romantic & 20th Century,* Level 8, page 18)

3. Write the name of a piece you have played that uses both polyphonic and homophonic texture. _____

Unit 14
Two Part Inventions

A **two part invention** is a polyphonic piece with two voices utilizing imitation at the octave. Certain melodic elements and the use of particular compositional devices characterize the structure of a two part invention.

Melodic Elements

- **Subject:** The subject is a melody that is an essential element in the structure of a composition. The subject is stated at the beginning of an invention in one voice and is immediately imitated by the other voice. The subject may be stated many times throughout the invention. It may be transposed, inverted, or have rhythmic or intervallic variations.
- **Countersubject:** The countersubject is a contrasting melody that is stated in the first voice immediately after the subject. The countersubject occurs as the second voice imitates the subject. The countersubject may be stated many times throughout the invention. It may be transposed, inverted, or have rhythmic or intervallic variations.
- **Motive:** A motive is a short melodic pattern that appears throughout a composition as a unifying element. It is distinguished from a subject by being much shorter and is often a fragment of of the subject.

Compositional Devices

- **Imitation:** Imitation is the immediate restatement of a subject or motive in another voice.
- **Sequence:** A sequence occurs when a subject or motive is repeated in the same voice at a higher or lower pitch.
- **Inversion:** A subject or motive is inverted when ascending intervals are changed into the corresponding descending intervals and vice versa (i.e: *up a 2nd - up a 2nd - down a 3rd* becomes *down a 2nd - down a 2nd - up a 3rd).*

Two Part Inventions by J. S. Bach

Johann Sebastian Bach (1685-1750) wrote fifteen two part inventions, each in a different key. In 1720, Bach began writing the *Clavier Büchlein für Wilhelm Friedemann Bach* to assist him in teaching his nine year old son. In addition to an explanation of clefs, ornaments and fingering, the book contains the first version of the two part inventions. Bach's goal was to teach students "...to play cleanly and in two parts...to achieve a cantabile style of playing and to acquire a taste for the elements of composition."

Bach's two part inventions are characterized by the melodic elements and compositional devices described above. Inventions 1, 2, 3, 4, 6, 7, 8 and 13 follow the "rule" of imitation at the octave with a clear presentation of subject and countersubject. Inventions 5, 9, 10, 11, 12, 14 and 15 are imitative in their structure, but do not feature strict imitation at the octave nor the formal presentation of subject and countersubject as described above.

Invention No. 13 by J. S. Bach

Invention No. 13 has two distinct rhythmic motives.

Rhythmic motive no. 1:   Rhythmic motive no. 2:

Rhythmic motive no. 1 sometimes appears with one of the following rhythmic variations:

or

In measures 6-7 and 11-12, the rhythmic motives are shortened to:

In measures 14-17, 19-21 and 23-25,
rhythmic motive no. 1 is lengthened to:

With few exceptions, the notes of the rhythmic motives are always broken chords, for example:

Measures 9-10, right hand

A minor   D7   G Major   CM7

The subject and countersubject overlap the rhythmic motives.

subject   countersubject   subject

subject   countersubject   subject
inversion

Invention No. 13 is on pages 35-37. Below each line of music are the chords formed by the notes of the broken chords in the music. The chords are written in close position in the bass staff, but include both the bass and treble staff notes in each measure of music. The inversion of each chord is determined by the lowest note of each broken chord in the music. When the 3rd or 5th of a seventh chord is omitted in the music, it is added into the chords below the music. The key signature is A minor, but there are modulations within the Invention. The various keys to which the music modulates are marked for you.

Study the music on pages 35-37 to complete the following exercises.

1. Write the Roman numerals and figured bass for each chord according to the indicated key. In measures 14-16 and 23, only write the chord names (do not analyze in a key with Roman numerals). Reminder: accidentals last the whole measure!

2. Mark each entrance of the subject and countersubject throughout the music with brackets.

Invention No. 13

J. S. Bach
(1685-1750)

A minor:

of

C Major:

(C Major)

G Major:

E minor:

(E minor)

(From E Natural minor)

The bass note for this chord is found on the first beat of measure 14.

Measures 14-16: Chord names only (no Roman numerals).

A minor: _____

Measure 23: Chord names only (no Roman numerals).

(A minor)

Unit 15
Sonata-Allegro Form

First movements of sonatas are usually written in a form called **sonata-allegro** or *first movement* form*. Sonata-allegro became the most important form of the Classical period and was brought to its highest level of sophistication in the sonatas by Haydn, Mozart and Beethoven.

Sonata-allegro is a ternary form. The three sections of sonata-allegro form are shown below.

1. **Exposition**
      A. First theme: tonic key
      B. Second theme:dominant key, or relative Major key if the movement is in a minor key.
      C. Closing theme (optional): dominant key, or relative Major key if the movement is in a minor key

2. **Development**
      Themes (and/or motives from themes) are presented in new keys.
      New themes may be added.

3. **Recapitulation**
      A. First theme: tonic key
      B. Second theme: tonic key
      C. Closing theme (optional): tonic key

A **coda** (ending) is sometimes included after the second theme or closing theme.

The relationship of keys is particularly important in sonata-allegro form. In the exposition, the first theme is in the tonic key and the second theme is in the dominant key or in the relative Major key if the movement is in a minor key. In the development, any or all of the themes may be used and they will "travel" through keys other than the tonic, dominant or relative keys. In the recapitulation, both the first and the second theme are in the tonic key. The use of the tonic key for the second theme in the recapitulation gives the music a sound of completion, or of returning "home".

The music on pages 40-43 is the first movement of the *Sonata, Op. 49, No. 1* by Ludwig van Beethoven (1770-1827). Study the music on pages 40-43 to answer these questions.

1. Name the key of the first theme.   _____

2. Name the form of minor scale used in the left hand in measure 2.   _____

3. Write the Roman numeral and figured bass for the chord on beat one in measure 2.   _____

4. Write the Roman numeral for the chord in measure 4.   _____

5. Write the Roman numeral and figured bass for the circled chord in measure 12.   ____ of ____

*The term first movement form, although correctly and frequently used, is somewhat misleading because sonata-allegro form is not limited to first movements. Sonata movements other than the first are sometimes written in sonata-allegro form. Sonata-allegro form is also used in symphonies and concertos.

6. Write the Roman numeral and figured bass for the circled chord in measure 13. _____

7. Name the key of the second theme. _____

8. Name the ornament used in measures 17, 19, 21, 22 and 25. _____

9. Write the Roman numeral and figured bass for the chord in measure 16. _____

10. Write the Roman numeral and figured bass for the chord in measure 17. _____

11. Write the Roman numeral and figured bass for the chord on beat two in measure 21. ___ of ___

12. Write the Roman numeral and figured bass for the chord in measure 22. _____

13. Write the Roman numeral and figured bass for the chords in measure 23. _____ _____
(There are two chords.)

14. Which theme is used in the Coda, first or second? _____

15. Which theme is used at the beginning of the Development, first or second? _____

16. Name the key from measures 34 to 47. _____

17. Name the key in measures 49 and 50. _____

18. Name the key beginning at measure 51. _____

19. Write the Roman numeral and figured bass for the chord in measure 51. _____

20. Write the Roman numerals and figured bass for the chords in measure 52. _____ _____
(There are two chords.)

21. From which theme is the circled motive in measures 54-55, first or second? _____

22. Is the circled motive in measures 54-55 changed from its original form through augmentation or diminution? _____

23. The right hand notes in measures 58-59 are an inversion of a motive in the first theme. Name the measures in which this motive appears in the Exposition. _____

24. In what measure does the Recapitulation begin? _____

25. In what measure does the second theme begin in the Recapitulation? _____

26. Name the key of the second theme in the Recapitulation. _____

27. In what measure does the Coda begin in the Recapitulation? _____

28. Name the chord in the last measure. _____

Sonata
Op. 49, No. 1

Ludwig van Beethoven
(1770-1827)

EXPOSITION

First Theme

Second Theme

43

GP668

Unit 16
Signs and Terms

Dynamics

TERM	SIGN	MEANING
pianississimo	*ppp*	very, very soft
pianissimo	*pp*	very soft
piano	*p*	soft
mezzo piano	*mp*	medium soft
mezzo forte	*mf*	medium loud
forte	*f*	loud
fortissimo	*ff*	very loud
fortississimo	*fff*	very, very loud
crescendo (cresc.)	<	gradually louder
diminuendo (dim.)	>	gradually softer
fortepiano	*fp*	loud, then immediately soft

Tempo

TERM	MEANING
adagio	slow
allegro	fast (also means cheerful, happy)
allegretto	somewhat fast (slower than allegro)
andante	walking tempo (flowing)
andantino	slightly faster than andante
animato	animated, with spirit
con moto	with motion
largo	stately, broad, a very slow tempo
lento	slow
moderato	moderately
presto	very fast
vivace	lively, quick
vivo	lively

Changing Tempo

accelerando (accel.)	gradually faster
allargando	broadening, gradually slower
a tempo	return to the original tempo
meno mosso	less motion, slower
piu mosso	more motion, faster
rallentando (rall., rallent.)	gradually slower
ritardando (rit.)	gradually slower
ritenuto	held back, suddenly slower

Character or Style

TERM	MEANING
cantabile	in a singing manner
con brio	with spirit
con fuoco	with fire
dolce	gently, sweetly
doloroso	sadly, sorrowfully
espressivo	expressively
---etto	little
giocoso	humorous
grazioso	gracefully
--ino	little
leggiero	lightly
meno	less
molto	much, very
pesante	heavily, ponderously
piu	more
poco	little
robusto	boldly, robustly
scherzando	playful
sempre	always
senza	without
simile	in a similar manner, same
spiritoso	spirited
subito	suddenly
tranquillo	peacefully, tranquil, calm

Articulation

TERM	SIGN	MEANING
accent		strong emphasis
legato		smooth, connected
sforzando	*sf* or *sfz*	sudden strong accent
sostenuto		sustained, legato
staccato		short, detached
tenuto		hold full value; slight emphasis

Additional Signs and Terms

Alberti bass: An accompaniment pattern using a three note chord. The notes of the chord are played bottom - top - middle - top.

Arpeggio: The notes of a chord played one after another instead of together. The notes of an arpeggio may be written out, or indicated by a wavy line to the left of the chord.

Chromatic Half Step: A half step with two notes of the same letter name (for example: C to C♯).

Diatonic Half Step: A half step with notes of different letter names (for example: C to D♭).

D. C. al Fine (da capo al fine): Play from the beginning to the *fine* (end).

Fermata ⌒ : Hold a note longer than its time value.

Grace Note ♪ : A grace note is printed in small type. It is not counted in the rhythm; it is played quickly, almost together with the next note.

m.d. (mano destra): Right hand.

m.s. (mano sinistra): Left hand.

Octave Sign *8va--------*
When the octave sign is placed over notes, play one octave (eight notes) higher than written.
When the octave sign is placed under notes, play one octave lower than written.

Opus (Op.): Work. The term is usually used with a number to indicate the chronological order of music written by a composer (Op. 1, Op. 2, Op. 3, etc.).

Pedal Sign └──────┘ : The pedal sign shows when to press and lift the damper (right) pedal.

tre corde: Release the soft (left) pedal.

una corda: Depress the soft (left) pedal.

Ornaments

Melodic Phrase Structure

Augmentation: The presentation of a melody or motive with the note values doubled.

Canon: A style of writing in which an extended melody is imitated strictly and entirely in one or more voices.

Diminution: The presentation of a melody or motive with the note values halved.

Imitation: The immediate restatement of a melody or motive in another voice or hand.

Motive (motif): A motive is a short melodic or rhythmic pattern that appears throughout a piece. When the motive appears in the music, it may begin on a different note, the rhythm may change slightly, or the motive may be inverted.

Repetition: Repetition occurs when a melodic or rhythmic pattern is repeated.

Sequence: A sequence occurs when a melodic pattern in repeated at a higher or lower pitch, usually a 2nd or 3rd above or below the original pattern.

Musical Forms

Binary Form: Music in binary form has two sections: section **A** and section **B**. Each section is usually repeated. The **A** section often ends on the dominant note, and the **B** section ends on the tonic.

Ternary form: Music written in ternary form has three sections: section **A,** section **B,** and a repeat of section **A.** The two sections are often contrasting in character or style.

Sonata: The sonata is a composition for piano which has separate sections called movements. The movements are usually contrasting in tempo and character.

Sonatina: The sonatina is a short sonata, usually designed for instruction. A sonatina may have one, two, or three movements. The movements are usually contrasting in tempo and character.

Sonata-Allegro Form: First movements of sonatas and sonatinas are frequently written in a form called "sonata-allegro" or *first movement* form:

   1. **Exposition** section
      A. first theme: tonic key
      B. second theme: dominant key, or relative Major if the piece is in minor key.
      C. closing theme (optional)

   2. **Development** section
      Themes are presented in new keys. New themes may be added.

   3. **Recapitulation** section
      A. first theme: tonic key
      B. second theme: tonic key
      C. closing theme (optional)

Rondo: Music in rondo form has a recurring theme (A) that appears between contrasting sections (B, C, etc.).

Texture in Music

Polyphonic Texture: Music with two or more independent parts or voices (melodies).

Homophonic Texture: Music with melody and accompaniment.

1. Write the term and meaning for each dynamic sign.

Sign	Term	Meaning
pp	_____	_____
mf	_____	_____
fp	_____	_____
◁_____	_____	_____

2. Write the meaning of each tempo term.

Term	Meaning
andante	_____
con moto	_____
vivace	_____
allegro	_____
presto	_____
accelerando	_____
piu mosso	_____

3. Write the term for each meaning.

Term	Meaning	Term	Meaning
_____	animated, with spirit	_____	gradually slower
_____	fast	_____	stately, broad, a very slow tempo
_____	moderately	_____	slightly faster than andante
_____	less motion, slower	_____	return to the original tempo

4. Write the meaning of each character or style term.

Term	Meaning
scherzando	_____
dolce	_____
simile	_____
cantabile	_____
senza	_____
leggiero	_____
sempre	_____

5. Match each term with its sign.

a. sforzando _____

b. Alberti bass _____

c. turn _____

d. arpeggio _____

e. mordent _____

f. appoggiatura _____

6. Match each term with its meaning.

a. m.d. _____ little

b. una corda _____ work

c. opus _____ right hand

d. ---etto _____ suddenly

e. piu _____ depress the soft (left) pedal

f. subito _____ more

Unit 17
The Four Periods of Music History

The history of music writing is generally divided into four basic periods: (1) Baroque, (2) Classical, (3) Romantic, and (4) 20ᵗʰ Century. Each period has certain styles which make it unique.

1. The Baroque Period (1600-1750)

The era from approximately 1600 to 1750 is known as the Baroque period. The term *baroque* was originally used to describe a style of art and architecture of highly decorative and extravagant design. The aesthetic ideal of the Baroque period permeated all aspects of European culture. Theater, painting, architecture and music were all characterized by grandiose concepts, dazzling effects, ornate design, and an overall dramatic quality.

Historical Context. Important historical events of the Baroque period were the Thirty Years War in Germany (1618-1648), the reign of Louis the XIV of France (1643-1715), the English Civil War (1642-1649), and the Restoration (1660). It was a time of worldwide colonization. Important names in science were Newton and Galileo. The leading philosophers were Descartes and Pascal. Prominent artists of the period include Dutch painters Rembrandt and Van Dyck, and the Spanish painter El Greco. The literature from the period include works by English writers Milton, Defoe, Addison, Swift, and Samuel Johnson, and French writers Racine and Moliere.

Baroque Music. Changes in style and form occurred continuously during the Baroque period, yet certain trends set Baroque music apart from that of other periods.

Basso Continuo. The lowest part in most Baroque music is the *basso continuo* (also called *thoroughbass*). It functions both as a melodic and harmonic bass. The basso continuo part is written in the bass staff with figured bass below the notes. It was the performer's responsibility to fill in the harmony according to the figured bass. This process is called *realizing* the figured bass.

Harmony. Figured bass reflected new harmonic concepts in music. Chords and inversions, authentic cadences, and chromaticism acquired a prominent role. Modulation and the use of seventh chords became commonplace.

Tonality. The Baroque period saw the maturation of the modern concepts of Major and minor tonality. Titles of compositions began to indicate keys (Sonata in D minor, Suite in A Major, etc.) and music began to convey a strong sense of tonal center.

Texture. The texture of Baroque music is predominantly polyphonic. The polyphony is harmonically oriented, and it reached its highest level of mastery in the music of Johann Sebastian Bach. The relative prominence of the bass line is also an aspect of Baroque texture. Homophonic texture exists in certain types of Baroque music where a single melodic line is supported by harmonic material.

Tempo and Dynamics. For the first time in history, some composers began to use tempo and dynamic markings in an attempt to convey the correct expression, emotional content or mood of the music. However, tempo and dynamic markings were limited and not used by all composers.

Improvisation. Improvisation played an important role in the performance of Baroque music. Musicians were highly trained in the art of improvising melodic ornaments, variations on a theme, cadenzas, and the realization of figured bass with complex polyphonic material.

Musical Forms. The most important form that evolved during the Baroque period was the *fugue*. The dance suite was also a prominent form developed during the Baroque period. Dance suite movements were most frequently in binary form. Additional styles of Baroque keyboard pieces include the *invention*, *prelude*, and *toccata*.

Baroque Composers

Bach, Johann Sebastian (Germany, 1685-1750)	Rameau, Jean-Philippe (France, 1683-1764)
Couperin, François (France, 1668-1733)	Scarlatti, Domenico (b. Italy 1685 - d.Spain 1757)
Daquin, Louis (France, 1694-1772)	Telemann, Georg Philipp (Germany, 1681-1767)
Handel, George Frideric (b. Germany 1685-d. England 1759)	

Baroque Keyboard Instruments. Precursors of the modern piano are the *clavichord* and *harpsichord*. The clavichord mechanism produced a tone by means of a small metal tangent attached to the end of the key which struck the strings from below. The tone was delicate and the instrument was used mostly in intimate settings. The harpsichord became the "concert grand" of the 18ᵗʰ century. The tone of this plucked keyboard instrument was fuller and had more carrying power than that of the clavichord. An early version of the harpsichord was constructed in 1503 by Giovanni Spinetti of Venice. Named after its inventor, the *spinet* (called the *virginal* in England) produced a tone by plucking the string with a quill. In France, the harpsichord was called the *clavecin*, and in Italy, the *cembalo* or *clavicembalo*. Later harpsichord makers added longer strings and various stops and pedals. By the mid-17th century harpsichords had two keyboards, with two or three strings for each pitch to produce a fuller tone.

Baroque composers adapted their compositions to the capabilities of the clavichord and harpsichord. Since the harpsichord was unable to produce gradual tone gradations (crescendos and diminuendos), composers wrote "echo" effects: a phrase played loud on one keyboard and then repeated softly on a second keyboard. The juxtaposition of loud and soft dynamics is called *terraced dynamics*. Because of the lack of sustaining power, especially of the harpsichord, numerous embellishments were added to "fill-in" the sound. Through the use of various stops and coupling or dampening of the strings a variety of effects could be made.

2. The Classical Period (1750-1825)

The 18th century encompasses several stylistic trends which overlap chronologically. It includes the diverse musical concepts of style and form of the late Baroque, Pre-Classical, and Classical periods. The years from 1750 to 1825 represent the rise and culmination of classicism in music.

Historical Context. The years from 1750 to 1825 were marked by the rise of democratic forces manifested in the French Revolution. Other military conflicts were the Seven Years' War (1756-1763), the French and Indian Wars in America, the conflict between England and the American colonies culminating in the Declaration of Independence (1776) and the American Revolution, the War of 1812, and the Napoleonic Wars in Europe. Important writers of the time include Voltaire and Rousseau. Artists of the period include Watteau, Goya, David, Gainsborough, and Copley. Achievements in science were the development of the first vaccine, the discoveries of oxygen, hydrogen, electromagnetic induction, and ultraviolet rays. The invention of the steam engine, cotton gin, electric motors and generators were factors in the Industrial Revolution, which began in England around 1760.

Pre-Classical Music. Music which represents the transition from the Baroque to Classical period is usually called Pre-Classical. Changes in concepts of form and style took place from approximately 1720 to 1750. No clear line of separation can be drawn between late Baroque, Pre-classical and early Classical music. A variety of styles often occur in works of the same composer. Basic changes include the abandonment of polyphonic texture in favor of homophonic texture, the disappearance of the basso continuo, and binary form replaced with ternary form.

Pre-Classical Composers

Bach, Johann Christian (Germany, 1735-1782)   Kirnberger, Johann Philipp (Germany, 1721-1783)
Bach, Carl Philipp Emanuel (Germany, 1714-1788)   Mozart, Leopold (Austria, 1719-1787)
Bach, Wilhelm Friedemann (Germany, 1710-1784)   Paradisi, Domenico (Italy, 1707-1791)
Benda, Georg (Germany, 1722-1795)

Classical Music. The word *classical* may be defined with three contrasting meanings: (1) the art and literature of ancient Greece, (2) the antonym of "popular" music, and (3) the era from approximately 1750 to 1825. It is the third definition that is used in music history. Classicism implies the ideals of the Apollonian cult of ancient Greece: objectivity, ethos, emotional restraint, and the balance and clarity of form. These ideals are reflected in the music of the Classical period.

Form. Ternary forms, particularly sonata-allegro form, were firmly established during the Classical period. Phrase structure was characteristically clear with well defined cadences, and phrases were shorter (usually four measures) than in Baroque music.

Texture. Classical music was usually in homophonic texture, often a single melodic line with accompaniment. The most typical accompaniment pattern was the *Alberti bass*, named for the Pre-Classical composer Domenico Alberti (1710-1740). Polyphonic texture did not disappear completely, however fugues and other polyphonic forms were rarely written. Another aspect of Classical texture was the prevalence of thin, light sonorities as opposed to the predominantly massive sounds of Baroque music.

Melodic Style. Classical melodies were more concise with more thematic unity than the long, continuous lines of Baroque music. Classical melodies were generally diatonic.

Harmony. Classical harmony was overall less complex than Baroque harmony. More emphasis was given to primary triads, and diatonic harmony was more typical than chromatic. Chords were usually triadic, and seventh chords were used sparingly.

Improvisation. The art of improvisation died out with the disappearance of the basso continuo. All harmony was written out. Composers became more specific and consistent with the indications of ornamentation, phrasing, dynamics, and other details formerly left to the discretion of the performer.

Absolute Music. The classical period favored what is called *absolute music*: music which does not attempt to describe extra-musical things nor include descriptive titles.

Classical Composers.

Beethoven, Ludwig van (Germany, 1770-1827)
Clementi, Muzio (b. Italy 1752 - d. England 1832)
Czerny, Carl (Austria, 1791-1857)
Haydn, Joseph (Austria, 1732-1809)

Kuhlau, Friedrich (b. Germany 1786 - d. Denmark 1832)
Mozart, Wolfgang Amadeus (Austria, 1756-1791)
Pleyel, Ignaz (France, 1757-1831)
Türk, Daniel Gottlob (Germany, 1756-1832)

Classical Period Pianos. The possibilities of combining the sustaining tone of the clavichord with the power of the harpsichord were no doubt alluring to musicians and keyboard builders of the 17th century. It is not surprising that three inventors working independently in different countries perceived the hammer action piano concept at about the same time: Cristofori in Italy (1709), Marius in France (1716), and Schroter in Germany (1717). Credit is given to Bartolomeo Cristofori, curator of musical instruments for the wealthy Medici family in Florence, for producing the first piano. Cristofori called his invention a *gravicembalo col piano e forte* (a keyboard instrument which can play soft and loud). The ability of the early piano to produce graded dynamics (crescendos and diminuendos), plus its sustaining quality appealed to composers and keyboard makers of the time. By about 1728, Cristofori had improved his pianoforte by constructing a much stronger case than had been used for harpsichords to withstand the increased strain of heavier strings. The action at this time resembled the basic mechanics of the modern piano: escapement device, a back check regulating the fall of the hammer, and a damper for each key. Pianoforte building was continued by craftsmen such as Gottfried Silbermann, and his pupils Johannes Zumpe and Americus Becker who went to London to establish English pianoforte building. One of Silbermann's most talented pupils, Johann Stein, carried Viennese pianoforte making to new heights, and his instruments were preferred by Mozart, Beethoven, and others. The early pianos were small and produced a light, delicate sound. Mozart's piano had a range of not quite five octaves. A piano built by Broadwood in 1817 for Beethoven had a range of six octaves. It is interesting to note that J. S. Bach played one of Silbermann's pianos, and although he praised its tone, he complained that it was too weak in the treble, and it was too hard to play (stiff action).

3. The Romantic Period (1825-1900)

The period of time from about 1825 to 1900 is known as the Romantic period. However, aspects of romanticism appeared before 1825 and continued well into the 20th century.

Historical Context. Progress in science and engineering (photography, the railway and steamboat, steel production, electricity, the telephone and telegraph, and other innovations) influenced the cultural, economic, political, and social orders of the 19th century. The growth of technology expanded the Industrial Revolution in Europe and created new social and economic dilemmas: the development of capitalism and the appearance of socialism. 19th century conflicts included the Crimean War (1854-1856), the Civil War in the United States (1861-1865), and the Franco-Prussian War (1870-1871). The most important movement in art was French Impressionism in the second half of the century, represented by Manet, Degas, Monet and Renoir. Related to this movement were the French symbolist poets Verlaine, Mallarmé, and Rimbaud. Prominent philosophers of the period included Hegel and Nietzsche. It was the era of great Romantic literature: Byron, Wordsworth, Dickens, Keats, Schiller, Goethe, Heine, E. T. A. Hoffmann, Lamartine, Hugo, Flaubert, Emerson, Poe, Mark Twain, and many others.

Romantic Music. Romanticism, perceived as the antonym of classicism, implies the Dionysian ideals of ancient Greece: pathos, subjectivity, emotionalism, placing instinct over reason and sentiment over precise form. The 19th century was a time characterized by the desire for individualism and nationalism. Composers of the Romantic period became more socially and economically independent, no longer relying on the patronage of the church or aristocracy. Music was generally composed for one of two settings: the concert hall or the more intimate salon. There were notable extremes in length of compositions: extensive works (concertos, symphonies, operas) and shorter works (songs and piano pieces). Composers developed a greater affinity with poetry, literature, and art, and as a result favored more descriptive or "programmatic" music. The virtuoso concert performer became a much admired musician, and virtuosity in music developed into a common trait. The Romantic period is a particularly rich era for pianists because it significantly expanded the amount of repertoire for the piano. Nationalism also became a notable trend. Composers deliberately incorporated national styles by using folklore as subjects for operas, songs, and programmatic music, often using folk tunes and folk styles in their compositions.

Melody. Melodies in Romantic music generally have qualities of personal warmth and expressiveness, a more lyrical style, and more flexible phrase structure.

Harmony. The harmonic language of the Romantic period became an important means for expression through expanded chord structure and progressions. Chromaticism and modulation played important roles, along with a freer treatment of dissonance and the frequent appearance of seventh chords.

Tonality. Music of the Romantic period was still tonal (in a central key). However, the feeling of being in a key was frequently obscured by extended chromatic modulations to unrelated keys. This trend paved the way for radically new concepts of tonality in the 20th century.

Texture. Music of the Romantic period was primarily in homophonic texture yet included frequent use of secondary melodies and/or polyphonic techniques. The sonority of Romantic music was notable for a marked increase in the richness of sound.

Dynamics. Composers of the Romantic period exploited the inherent possibilities of dynamics for emotional expression. It became characteristic of the period to use a wide range of dynamic levels between loud and soft and extensive use of crescendo and diminuendo.

Form. Content and subjective expression became more important than strict musical form. As a result, forms such as binary, ternary, sonata-allegro, rondo, etc., were generally freer, more variable, and often less distinct than in the Classical period. Short piano pieces were often given descriptive titles and are called *character pieces*. They include pieces with such titles as *arabesque, ballad, intermezzo, nocturne, rhapsody, impromptu, bagatelle, songs without words*, and descriptive titles such as *Venetian Boat Song, Butterfly, March of the Dwarfs*, etc. Stylized dances such as the *waltz, mazurka*, and *polonaise* became a significant portion of the piano repertoire. The *etude*, basically a study featuring some technical aspect of performance (scales, arpeggios, octave, chords, etc.) was composed as a virtuoso piece for concert audiences.

Romantic Composers.

Brahms, Johannes (Germany, 1833-1897)

Burgmüller, Friedrich (b. Germany 1806-d. France 1874)

Heller, Stephan (Germany, 1814-1888)

Chopin, Frédéric (b. Poland 1810- d. France 1849)

Grieg, Edvard (Norway, 1843-1907)

Liszt, Franz (Hungary, 1811-1886)

Mendelssohn, Felix (Germany, 1809-1847)

Schubert, Franz (Austria, 1797-1828)

Schumann, Robert (Germany, 1810-1856)

Spindler, Fritz (Germany, 1817-1905)

Streabbog, Jean Louis (France, 1835-1886)

Tchaikovsky, Peter Ilyich (Russia, 1840-1893)

Romantic Period Pianos. The period of 1760 to 1830 was one of great activity in the development of the piano. The French piano builders Sebastien and Erard developed an instrument with greater tone using a larger sound board (1776-1777). Because of the piano's capacity for sonority, dynamic range, and gradations between loud and soft, it became the Romantic instrument of choice. It provided composers and performers with possibilities of emotional expression ranging from intimate to grandiose, from delicate lyricism to bombastic showiness. The damper pedal enabled composers to experiment with new harmonic effects, and the improved keyboard mechanism stimulated new idioms, technics, and virtuosity.

4. The 20th Century (1900-2000)

The 20th century is an era in which the rapidity and significance of changes are unparalleled in history. Events and developments in political, social, scientific, and cultural history profoundly influenced the course of music.

Historical Context. Two global wars in the first half of the 20th century had powerful impacts on world history: World War I (1914-1918) and World War II (1939-1945). Each conflict was followed by an effort to establish world government: the League of Nations (1920-46) and the United Nations (established in 1946). The Bolshevik Revolution in 1917 marked the emergence of Communism and of Russia as a world power. Conflicts since the mid-century were the Korean War (1950-1953), the Arab-Israeli conflict, and the Vietnam wars. A political and ideological struggle between the Soviet Union and the United States after World War II was known as the Cold War, a period of nonmilitary activity, but one marked by a major armaments race.

Tremendous advances in science and engineering and their application to industry affected social, economic, and cultural history. Extensive progress took place in biology, chemistry, physics, and astronomy. Remarkable developments in technology were made in the areas of communication, transportation, and medicine. Some specific innovations include radio, television, atomic energy, jet propulsion, computers, antibiotics, exploration of space and of suboceanic areas, and, especially relevant to music, high-fidelity sound transmission.

As with all periods in history, the spirit of the times is reflected in the arts. 20th century trends include frequent and rapid changes, and experimentation with new forms. A general trend away from realism and toward abstract and subjective expression is particularly apparent in the visual arts. Important trends in art include expressionism, cubism, surrealism, pop art, minimal art, and conceptual art. Styles in literature, poetry, and theater also reflect the era: social protest, existentialism, pessimism and despair, absurdity, and intentional "shock value" are distinct traits.

20th Century Music. From a historical point of view, the study of 20th century music poses a number of problems not encountered in previous periods. So far, no satisfactory name has been devised (comparable with Baroque, Classical, or Romantic) for 20th century music. The expression "contemporary period" is frequently used, yet is rather misleading since it implies that which is current, as opposed to that which was heard in previous decades of the 20th century. The expression "modern music" is also frequently used, but its implications are so variable that it is almost meaningless. Due to the enormous quantity of music written since 1900, the extraordinary diversity of trends, styles and technics, and the rapidity and frequency of change, it is difficult to perceive and evaluate 20th century music as a coordinated whole. Unlike previous periods, no single style represents the 20th century, or even a appreciable portion of it. The elements of melody, harmony, tonality, texture, rhythm, and form are so complex and varied in 20th century music that they virtually preclude the systematic analysis that can be applied to the music of previous periods.

Several important styles emerged among the diversity of music in the 20th century. Some styles are more prominent than others, and some of longer duration than others. The various styles of 20th century music frequently overlap in their development and are not necessarily in chronological order. Also, they are often not distinctly separate developments. The unique character of one composer may be a composite of more than one style. Several of the important styles are Late Romanticism, Impressionism, Neo-Classicism, and Jazz.

Late Romantic Music. While revolutionary new styles were appearing in the early decades of the 20th century, trends of the Romantic period prevailed. Subjectivity, emotionalism, and programmatic music were traits that remained even in compositions which used new harmonies, rhythms, and tonalities.

Late Romantic Composers

Ernst von Dohnanyi (Hungary, 1877-1960)	Edward MacDowell (USA, 1860-1908)
Anatol Liadov (Russia, 1855-1914)	Sergei Rachmaninoff (Russia, 1873-1943)

Impressionist Music. Impressionism, often referred to as a "transitional period", was the first important trend leading to the changing styles of the 20th century. It paralleled the French movements in painting and poetry, and was largely a reaction against the Romantic period. Although Impressionism shares some common traits with Romantic music (it is generally subjective and programmatic), it abandoned traditional compositional technics in several ways. It may be described as having a high degree of delicacy, vagueness of form, and generally a "luminous fog" atmosphere. Specific technics include the use of open chords (5ths and octaves without 3rds), parallel chords and other unconventional chord progressions, whole tone scales, and freer treatment of meter.

Impressionist Composers.

Claude Debussy (France, 1862-1918)	Maurice Ravel (France, 1875-1937)
Francis Poulenc (France, 1899-1963)	Eric Satie (France, 1866-1925)

Neo-Classical Music. Neo-classicism is one of the most prominent and prevailing styles in music of the 20th century. It appeared about 1920, and continues through the entire century. Neo-classical music uses pre-romantic period ideals of objectivity, and clarity of form. It also revives polyphonic textures and forms of the Baroque period (fugue, toccata, etc.) while using 20th century concepts of harmony, melody, tonality, and rhythm.

Neo-Classical Composers

Paul Hindemith (Germany, 1895-1963)	Gian Carlo Menotti (Italy, 1911 - 2007)
Norman Dello Joio (USA, 1913 - 2008)	Sergei Prokofiev (Russia, 1891-1953)
Dmitri Kabalevsky (Russia, 1904-1987)	Igor Stravinsky (Russia, 1882-1971)
Aram Khachaturian (Russia, 1903-1978)	Alexander Tcherepnin (Russia, 1899-1977)

Jazz. Particularly a 20th century phenomenon, and primarily an American innovation in popular music, Jazz is an important style which has influenced many trends of serious composition. In its broadest definition, Jazz is improvised instrumental dance music. However, the variety of Jazz styles preclude summation in one concise category. The various types of Jazz include *Ragtime, Blues, Dixieland, Big Band, Swing, Boogie-Woogie, Bop, Progressive Jazz, Cool Jazz, Third-Stream,* and *Rock and Roll.* As well as influencing the myriad of trends of popular music of the 20th century, many "classical" composers have incorporated Jazz elements into their music.

20th Century Compositional Techniques. In addition to the various new styles of music discussed above, there are significant changes in compositional techniques in music of the 20th century. These changes are evident primarily in the elements of rhythm, melody, harmony, and tonality. However, it should be understood that not all music of the 20th century is a reflection of radical change in all respects. Any 20th century composition may have one or two elements that reflect 20th century technics, and not necessarily to the extreme. The music of the 20th century ranges from ultra-conservative to avant-garde, most of which lies somewhere between the two extremes.

Meter and Rhythm. Composers of the 20th century sought new metric and rhythmic effects. In general, rhythm is used with more complexity, variety, and flexibility. Odd-numbered time signatures such as $\frac{5}{2}$ and $\frac{7}{4}$ are commonly found. Asymmetrical groupings of beats are used to create rhythmic effects. For example, in $\frac{7}{8}$, beats may be felt in patterns such as 3-2-2 or 2-2-3. Occasionaly, the time signature may be written as $2+\frac{2}{8}+3$. In a more dramatic attempt at rhythmic flexibility, some composers omitted bar lines altogether.

Melody. Although many melodies in 20th century music are conservative, certain melodic characteristics are distinctly 20th century innovations. More extreme melodic styles include *disjunct melodies* (wide leaps from one note to the next), *angularity* (alternating upward and downward direction), and the use of dissonant intervals. Unconventional scales such as the *whole tone scale, pentatonic scale*, and *modal scales* also contribute to 20th century melodic styles.

Harmony. No element of 20th century music manifests more radical change than harmony. The tertian construction of chords (chords built with intervals of 3rds), such as triads and seventh chords, was augmented with the addition of more 3rds, resulting in 9th, 11th, and 13th chords. New types of 20th century chord construction include *quartal harmony* (chords built in 4ths), *tone clusters* and *polychords* (two or more different chords used simultaneously). Traditional chord progressions are largely abandoned in 20th century music and often replaced with arbitrary progressions, frequently involving chords with roots not related to the key. 20th century harmonic effects are often created with simple triads moving in parallel motion. One of the most distinct characteristics of 20th century harmony is the extent and degree to which dissonance is used. Unlike conventional harmony of the Baroque, Classical and Romantic periods, resolution of dissonance is not a prerequisite.

Tonality. Towards the end of the Romantic period, tonality (the feeling of being in a key, or gravitating towards a tonic note) was often obscured with increased chromaticism and prolonged modulations. Music of the 20th century departs further from traditional tonal concepts. 20th century innovations include *bitonality* (the use of two keys at the same time) and *polytonality* (the use of three or more keys at the same time) and *atonality* (the absence of any tonal center or key feeling). New scale constructions and the prolonged used of dissonance also contribute to tonal ambiguity.

Serialism. Serial music is constructed on the basis of a recurrent series of notes, rhythms, dynamics or other elements. Serialism first appeared in the 1920's with the development of the *twelve-tone row*. Serialism is related to both atonality and new concepts of form and structure in music.

20th Century Composers. Although names of composers were included in the preceding discussions of the various 20th century musical styles, many 20th century composers use a variety of styles and techniques and defy exact categorization. Listed here are a number of significant composers not named in the aforementioned text.

Agay, Denes (USA, 1911 - 2007)	Ginastera, Alberto (Argentina, 1916-1983)
Barber, Samuel (USA, 1910-1981)	Muczynski, Robert (USA, 1929 - 2010)
Bartók, Béla (b. Hungary 1881 d. New York 1945)	Pinto, Octavio (Brazil, 1890-1950)
Bastien, James (USA, 1934 - 2005)	Rocherolle, Eugénie (USA, 1936-)
Britten, Benjamin (England, 1913-1976)	Shostakovich, Dmitri (Russia, 1906-1975)
Copland, Aaron (America, 1900-1990)	Tansman, Alexander (B. Poland 1897, d. France 1986)
Gershwin, George (USA 1898-1937)	Turina, Joaquin (Spain, 1882-1949)
Gillock, Willian (USA, 1917-1996)	Villa-Lobos, Heitor (Brazil, 1887-1959)

Unit 18
Ear Training

Practice #1

Listen as your teacher plays one interval from each pair. Circle the one you hear.

Listen as your teacher plays one triad from each pair. Circle the one you hear.

9. Listen as your teacher plays one of the scales below. Check (✓) the one you hear.

_____ Natural   _____ Harmonic   _____ Melodic

Listen as your teacher plays one chord progression from each pair. Check (✓) the one you hear.

12. Listen as your teacher plays one of the phrases below. Check (✓) the one you hear.

13. Listen as your teacher plays one of the phrases below. Check (✓) the one you hear.

Practice #2

Listen as your teacher plays one interval from each pair. Circle the one you hear.

Listen as your teacher plays one triad from each pair. Circle the one you hear.

9. Listen as your teacher plays one of the scales below. Check(✓) the one you hear.

_____ Natural   _____ Harmonic   _____ Melodic

Listen as your teacher plays one chord progression from each pair. Check (✓) the one you hear.

12. Listen as your teacher plays one of the phrases below. Check (✓) the one you hear.

13. Listen as your teacher plays one of the phrases below. Check (✓) the one you hear.

Unit 19
Sight Reading

The best way to become a good sight reader is to read new music every day.

1. Before you sight read, look through the entire piece and observe:
   - the key signature
   - the time signature
   - the clef signs
   - dynamics
   - accidentals
   - slurs, ties, staccatos, accents, etc.
   - rhythmic and melodic patterns

2. Find the first note and finger number for each hand.

3. Play slowly.
   - Use a metronome to keep a steady beat.
   - Count one measure aloud before you begin to play.
   - Continue to count aloud as you play.

4. Keep your eyes on the music.
   - Avoid looking up and down from the music to your hands.
   - Look ahead to see what is next.

5. Keep going, even if you make some mistakes; avoid going back to "fix" anything.

6. After you sight read, evaluate your playing.
   - Were the notes and rhythm correct?
   - Were the dynamics and articulation markings clear and distinct?
   - Did the music continue to move forward as you maintained a steady beat?

7. Sight read the music again.
   - Concentrate on correcting any previous mistakes.
   - Set a goal for a perfect performance by the third reading.

Allegro

Vivace

Review Test

1. Write these key signatures.

E Major   D♭ Major   F minor   G♯ minor   E♭ Major   B Major   C minor

2. Draw these scales one octave, ascending.

G♭ Major   A Major

B harmonic minor   D natural minor

3. Add the accidentals needed to form the G melodic minor scale.

G melodic minor

4. Draw a note above the one given to form each interval.

d5   A4   M3   m6   M7   d7   A2

5. Add bar lines to divide this rhythm into measures. Write the counts on the line below the staff.

6. Draw these triads.

G dim. 6   B♭ Aug.   F♯ minor $^6_4$ D♭ Major $^6_4$ A Major 6   F Aug. $^6_4$

7. Draw the dominant seventh chord for each key.

A Major   G minor   B Major   F minor   D Major

V7   V$^6_5$ V$^4_3$ V$^6_5$ V$^4_2$

8. Draw these diminished seventh chords.

G°7   A°$^4_3$ D°$^6_5$ F°7   C♯°$^4_2$

9. Write this chord progression.

B♭ Major

I   IV$^6_4$ ii   V$^6_5$ vi 6

10. Draw a whole tone scale from the given note.

11. Write a diminution of the melody below.

Diminution

Gigue

From "Suite in A"

Georg Philipp Telemann
(1681-1767)

of

Study the music on page 62 to answer the following questions.

12. The music on page 62 is a Gigue from a dance suite. During what period of
    music history were dance suites developed as a prominent form?   _____

13. Write the last name of the composer of this Gigue.   _____

14. Did the composer live during the same period of music history that you answered
    in question number 12?   _____

15. What is the tempo of this piece? Write the Italian word and its meaning.   _____ _____

16. Name the Major key signature of the piece.   _____

17. No time signature is given. What should the time signature be?   _____

18. What is the name of the ornament in measure 1?   _____

19. Draw the notes for the correct performance of the ornament in measure 1.

20. What is the texture of this piece?   _____

21. Name the compositional device used in measures 1-4.   _____

22. Draw the rhythm of the subject.

23. Draw the rhythm of the countersubject.

24. Name the boxed interval in measure 5.   _____

25. There are four more intervals in the treble staff of the same quality you named in
    question 24. Write the measure numbers where these intervals are found. Circle
    the measure number in which it is a harmonic interval.   _____ _____ _____ _____

26. Write the Roman numeral and figured bass for the chord in measure 12.   _____ of _____

27. To what key does the music modulate at measure 13?   _____

28. What is the relationship (scale degree name) of the new key to the original key? _____

29. Does the music cadence at measure 36 in the same key you named in question 27? _____

Answer questions 30-34 according to the key to which the music modulated in measure 13.

30. Write the Roman numeral and figured bass for the chord in measure 20.   _____ of _____

31. Write the Roman numeral and figured bass for the boxed chord in measure 27.   _____

32. Write the Roman numeral and figured bass for the boxed chord in measure 28.   _____ of _____

33. Write the Roman numerals and figured bass on the lines under the staff in
    measures 28-31 and measures 34-36.

34. Name the cadence in measures 35-36.   _____

35. What is the term for the use of the bass staff note (B) in measures 22-28?   _____

36. Name the notes of the diatonic half step in measure 6.   _____ to _____

37. There is only one chromatic half step in the music. In what measure is it?   _____

38. Name the boxed interval in measure 30.   _____

39. What is the meaning of *m.s.* in measure 33?   _____

64

40. Write the names of three pieces that you have played from the Baroque period. Name the composer of each piece and include the birth and death dates of each composer and the country in which the composer was born. Then, describe two features of each piece (such as form, texture, style, etc.) that are characteristic of music from the Baroque period.

Title _____

Composer _____ b. _____ d. _____ Country _____

Two Features Characteristic of Baroque Music _____

_____

Title _____

Composer _____ b. _____ d. _____ Country _____

Two Features Characteristic of Baroque Music _____

_____

Title _____

Composer _____ b. _____ d. _____ Country _____

Two Features Characteristic of Baroque Music _____

_____

41. Write the names of three pieces that you have played from the Classical period. Name the composer of each piece and include the birth and death dates of each composer and the country in which the composer was born. Then, describe two features of each piece (such as form, texture, style, etc.) that are characteristic of music from the Classical period.

Title _____

Composer _____ b. _____ d. _____ Country _____

Two Features Characteristic of Classical Music _____

_____

Title _____

Composer _____ b. _____ d. _____ Country _____

Two Features Characteristic of Classical Music _____

_____

Title _____

Composer _____ b. _____ d. _____ Country _____

Two Features Characteristic of Classical Music _____

_____